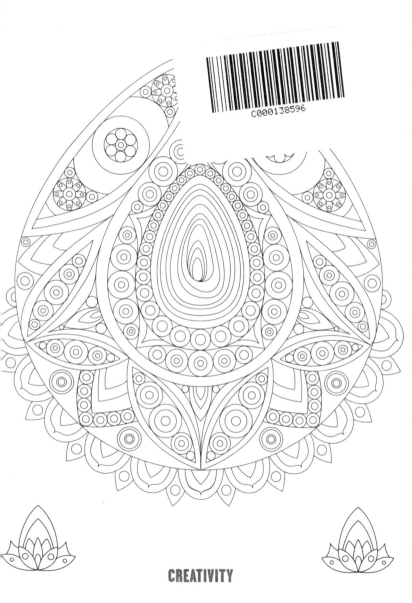

CREATIVITY

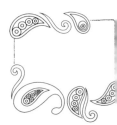

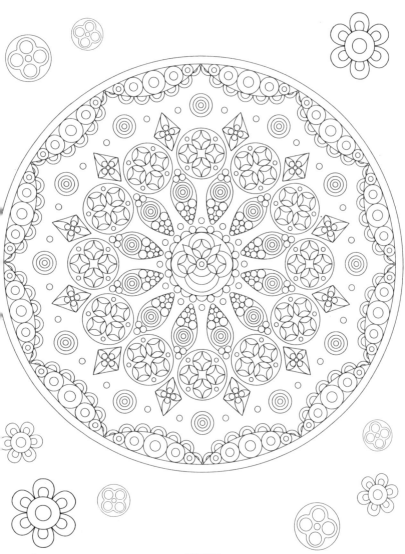

GRACE

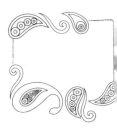

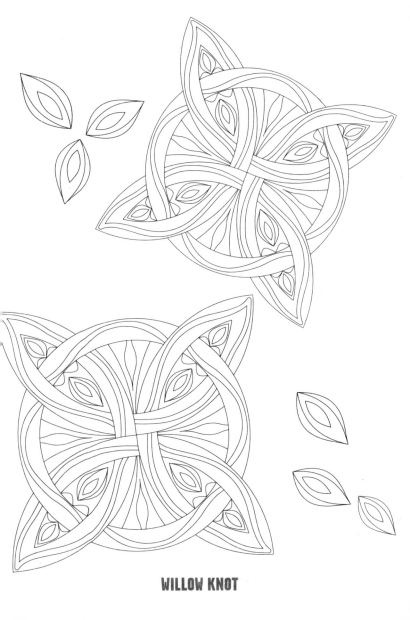

WILLOW KNOT

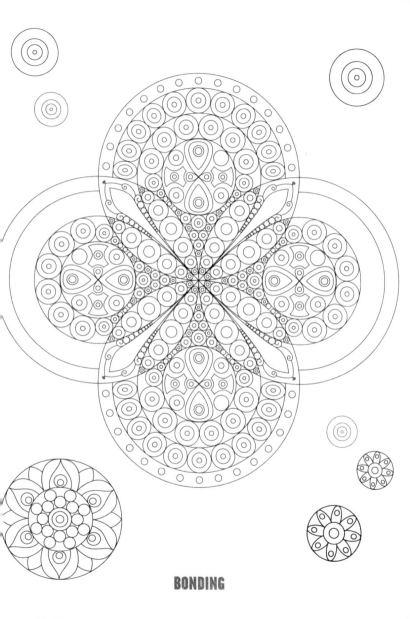

BONDING

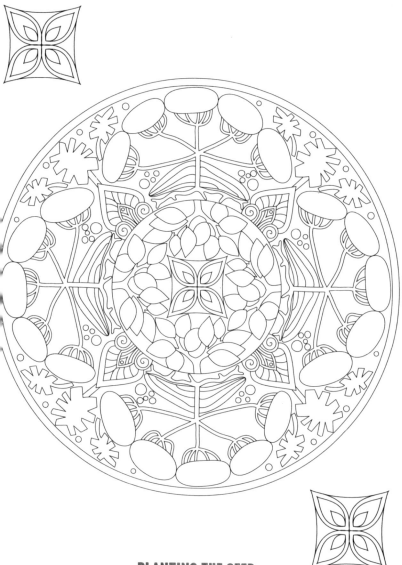

PLANTING THE SEED

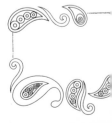

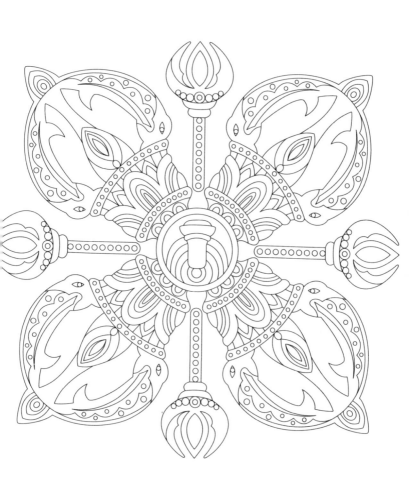

MASCULINITY

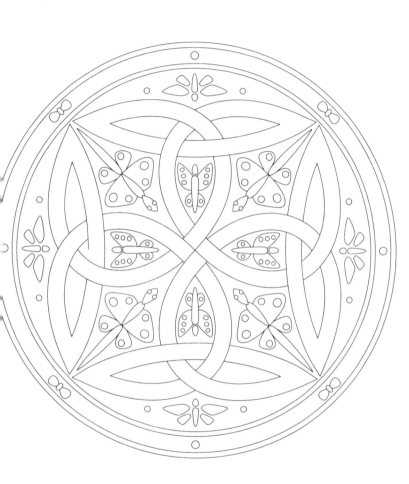

INTEGRATION

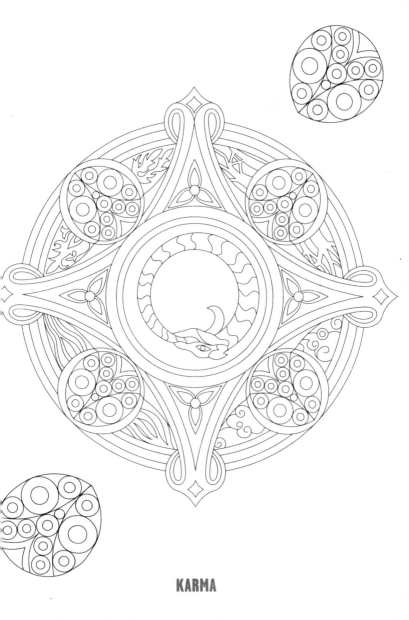

KARMA

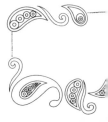

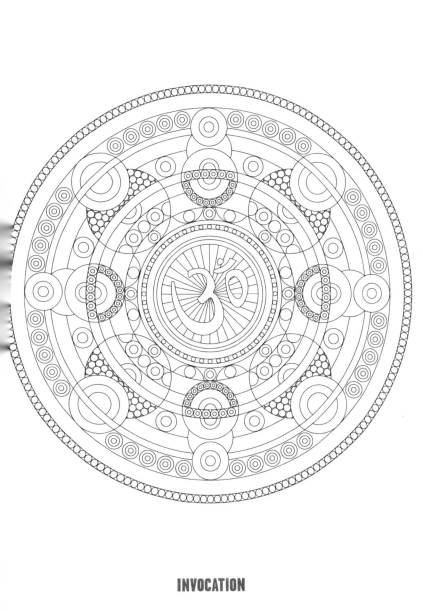

INVOCATION

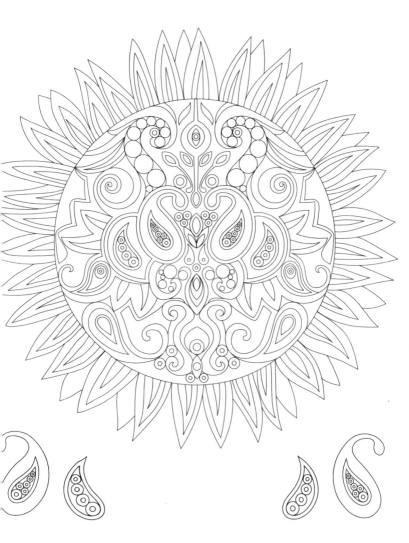

PERSONAL POWER

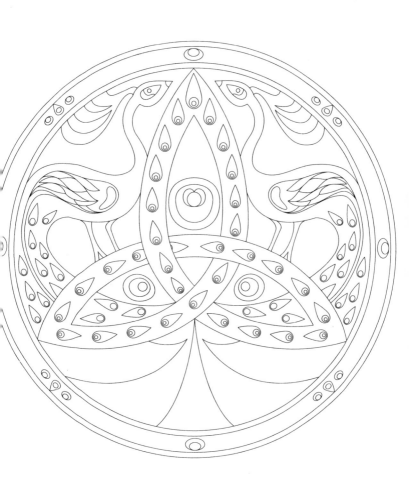

OSTARA

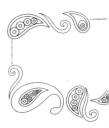

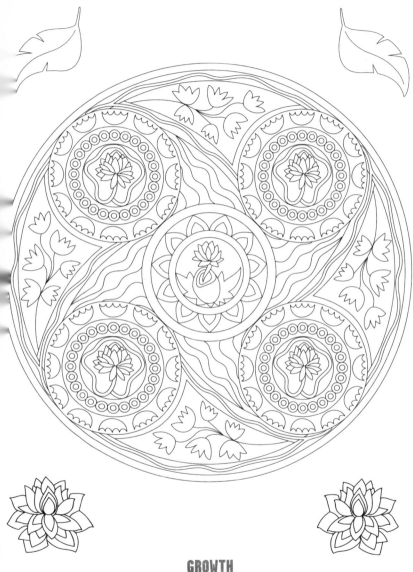

GROWTH

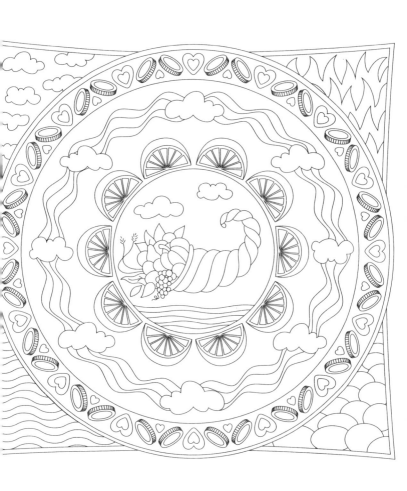

CORNUCOPIA

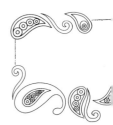

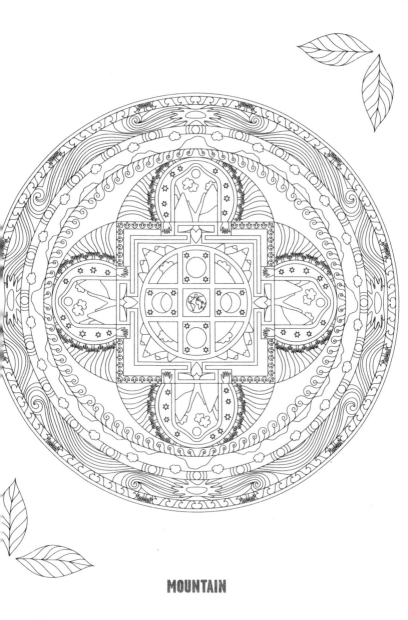

MOUNTAIN

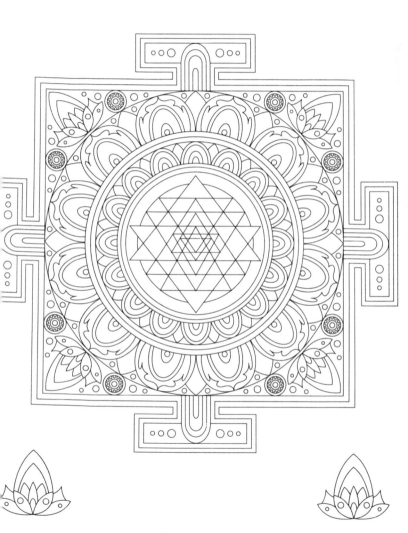

SHRI YANTRA

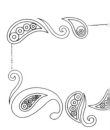

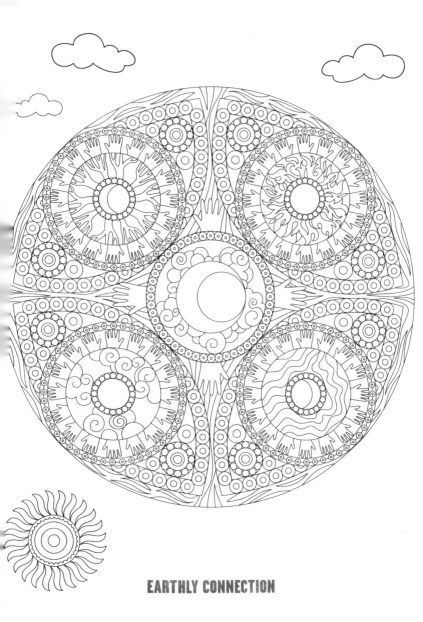

EARTHLY CONNECTION

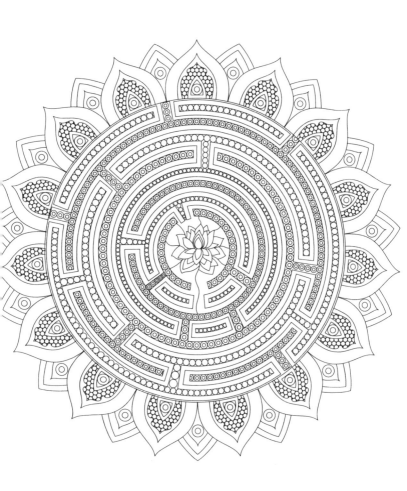

BOREDOM

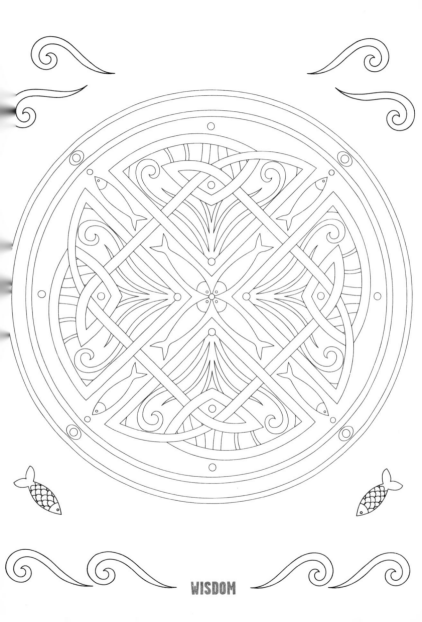

WISDOM

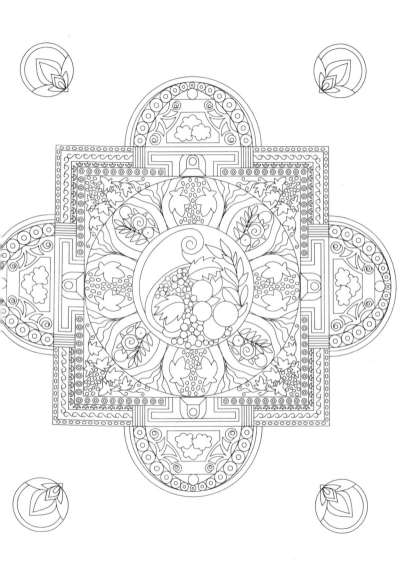

ABUNDANCE

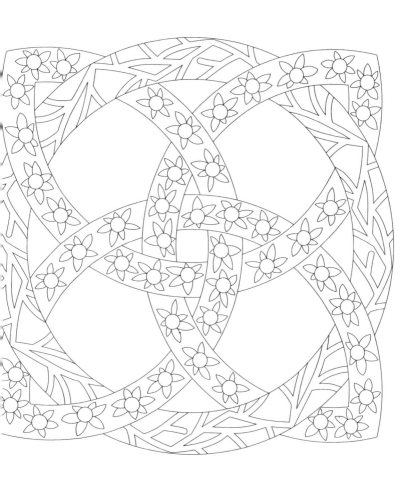

ENERGY